The Safest Place Possible

A Guide to Healing and Transformation

COMPANION WORKBOOK

Debbie Mirza

The Safest Place Possible Companion Workbook.
Copyright © 2017 by Debbie Mirza and
Safe Place Publishing, Monument, CO

DebbieMirza.com

Author photograph by Abby Mortenson, Love Roots Photography

Although the author and publisher have made every effort to ensure that the information in this book was correct at press time, the author and publisher do not assume and hereby disclaim any liability to any party for any loss, damage, or disruption caused by errors or omissions, whether such errors or omissions result from negligence, accident, or any other cause.

This book is not intended as a substitute for the medical advice of physicians. The reader should regularly consult a physician in matters relating to his/her health and particularly with respect to any symptoms that may require diagnosis or medical attention.

ISBN 978-0-9986213-2-6
eISBN 978-0-9986213-3-3

Contents

About Debbie Mirza...

Debbie is a life coach (trained by Dr. Martha Beck, best-selling author and columnist for O Magazine). Seeking out ways of healing emotionally, physically, and spiritually, has been in her DNA for a long time. As a life coach, her passion is helping others uncover their true selves and live life with more love, peace, clarity, strength, and purpose.

Debbie combines her intuitive and empathic gifts with practical tools in her coaching sessions. She is able to pick up on things people are feeling, and many times has a knowing of what they need to hear. This mix is quite powerful with helping people make big shifts in their lives. Debbie loves helping her clients see what makes them special, and how beautiful they really are.

What People Say About Debbie

"Debbie has this unique ability to look you right in the eye and probe you, ever so gently, to focus on what is holding you back on so many levels. She is non-threatening, yet has the ability to make you really face your uncertainties, insecurities — whatever it is holding you back from being the authentic self you want to be or whatever is blocking you — and then guiding you towards your own resolutions, not just telling you what you might want to hear. She helps you find the solution that works only for you; she is very perceptive with others and picks up on individual energies very quickly, to a degree that amazes me. She is always spot on. She is direct but compassionate and insightful in her spiritual guidance. In my session with her, I felt my stress and reluctance melt away and was able to get to the root of what was holding me back. She truly has a gift."

—Sasha C.

"Debbie has a way of weeding through confusing thoughts and feelings and getting to the heart of what is really going on. She has helped me get "unstuck" in some areas of my life with which I had struggled for years. I am amazed at the difference even one session with her made in the way I am living life now. She listens with such compassion; and the tools she uses, combined with her incredible intuition, have been truly life-changing for me. When I talk with Debbie, I feel as if my true self has been invited out to be heard."

— Liz B.

This **Companion Workbook** to **The Safest Place Possible: A Guide to Healing and Transformation** shares some of the exercises Debbie uses with her coaching clients, helping them discover their natural rhythm and more deeply connect with their authenticity.

The Safest Place Possible

Dear Lovely One,

This companion workbook is here for you; to help you connect with yourself in a loving and tender way.

I have taken concepts from my book, **The Safest Place Possible: A Guide to Healing and Transformation**, and created exercises so you can have the opportunity to implement the things I talk about in the book.

Some of the chapter titles in this companion workbook directly relate to those in the book so you can easily see when the exercise is based on content from that chapter.

You are welcome to use this in tandem with reading my book, or after you have read it.

There are extra pages at the end of each exercise for you to have more space to journal. You may have thoughts and feelings that came up for you as you did the exercises; inspired ideas, things you discovered that felt really good to you. If you are a creative, artistic person this can be a great place to add art to help you illustrate, express, and love yourself in out of the box ways. You make the rules. This is your special place to be you.

I adore you, I support you, and would love to meet you someday and hear about your own journey to peace within yourself.

Your friend,
Debbie Mirza

Effortless Value

I hope you know how lovely you are, dear reader.
I hope you know that just your being here is enough.

Exercise: List 10 reasons you are valuable even if you never accomplished anything, just by being you. (If this is hard for you, think of your best friend, someone you love, your child. How would you answer this question if it were about them? I have a hunch the same is true about you)

1.

2.

3.

4.

5.

6.

7.

8.

9.

10.

DebbieMirza.com   The Safest Place Possible

More About Effortless Value

The Beauty of Emotions

May you embrace all your feelings today.
May you be with yourself in a whole new way,
knowing you are beautiful just the way you are.
You are colorful and salty, and I'm so glad you're here.

This is an exercise that will take you out of your left brain. Allow this to be playful. Go with the first thing that pops into your head and trust that. You may want to close your eyes after you read the question and see what you hear. For me, this has a meditative feel to it. Take a few deep breaths before you start to help calm your mind.

You are now going to have a conversation with your emotions. You will be amazed how easily the answers come and intrigued by what you hear.

If you find this difficult, try asking in third person. For instance, I would ask "How are you here to help Debbie?" Sometimes this helps by allowing us to become an observer.

I also love adding, "thank you" after I get an answer.

Exercise: Answer the questions below with the first thought that comes to you.

1. Anger, how are you here to help me?

2. Sadness, how are you here to help me?

3. Grief, how are you here to help me?

4. Fear, how are you here to help me?

5. Anxiety, how are you here to help me?

6. Jealousy, how are you here to help me?

More About The Beauty of Emotions

My Teenage Sensei

What are you ready to let go of?

What are thoughts/beliefs/ways of being that are no longer serving you?

They deplete you of energy and make you feel bad about yourself.

Exercise: Write down 10 things you are ready to let go of. If you would like to go even further with this, you could write them on a separate piece of paper and burn them in a fire as a symbolic ceremony for yourself. You could even have friends join you in support of this beautiful transition you are making.

1.

2.

3.

4.

5.

6.

7.

8.

9.

10.

DebbieMirza.com   The Safest Place Possible

More About My Teenage Sensei

Snow White and Red Rose

1. Where in your life do you need Snow White to come forward and love and nurture you? What would that look like for you?

2. Where in your life do you need the fieriness of Rose Red to help you? What would that look like for you?

3. What would your life look like if you were to let go of the "perfect" picture and build it in a way that works for you, that is suited for your beautiful self? What would change for you?

More About Snow White and Red Rose

Ho'oponopono

Much love and kindness to you today as you get closer and closer to the beauty and peace that rests within you.

1. What is one thing you don't like about yourself? With this in mind say, "I'm sorry, please forgive me, I love you, thank you."

2. Think about someone who is affecting you in a negative way and say, "I'm sorry, please forgive me, I love you, thank you."

3. What is something that is causing you to feel a lot of stress right now? With this in mind say, "I'm sorry, please forgive me, I love you, thank you."

More About Ho'oponopono

_____

_____

_____

_____

_____

_____

_____

_____

_____

_____

_____

DebbieMirza.com The Safest Place Possible

Photo Albums

I hope you take the time to just be, when you need to, when you are feeling overwhelmed, uninspired, lost, in need of love and attention. You are worth the time. Being still, connecting with your true self, is some of the most important work you will do in this life. May you feel loads of love, tenderness, and healing today.

Exercise: Pull out a photo album with pictures of you in it, or look up pictures stored on your computer. Look at yourself and remember what you were feeling at that time. Then speak kindly and tenderly to yourself as you continue to look at the picture of you.

What is it that you needed to hear at that time from someone who loves you unconditionally and wants the best for you? Speak those words now and feel the healing take place in your body.

Well done lovely.

More About Photo Albums

Healing Your Inner Child

You deserve love, healing, and
the freedom to be your full self.

Intuitive Exercise: Think about something in your life that you feel stressed about or sad about. Close your eyes and ask yourself, "How old am I?" and go with whatever number you hear or see.

See yourself as that age as your eyes remain closed. Ask your younger self if she/he would like to sit on your lap, or maybe sit next to you. Go with whatever they feel they want to do.

Ask your younger self questions like, "what are you scared of right now?" and whatever else might come to you to ask. Remember, you are incredibly wise and unconditionally loving right now. This is the voice that will be speaking to the younger you that needs validation, reassurance, guidance, and hope.

Let yourself have a conversation with her/him. You will notice your body relaxing the more you help your inner child.

Write down anything that stood out to you from your conversation that you would like to remember below:

More About Healing Your Inner Child

Mom

I hope you can do something for yourself today that a loving mom, or mum, would do for you.

Loving Mom Exercise #1: Where are you being hard on yourself right now? Soothe yourself with the words of my Mom, "I can understand how you would feel that way." Say this all day long to whatever comes up for you today.

Loving Mom Exercise #2: If you could be a calming, loving, nurturing Mom to yourself today, what is one thing you would do for you that a Mom would do for her daughter or son? Do that one thing today and feel those loving arms around you.

More About Mom

DebbieMirza.com The Safest Place Possible

Spiritual Closet

Wherever you are in your search, I am with you there. You are not alone. I'm proud of you for asking the difficult questions. I'm proud of you for daring to think for yourself. And I love knowing you are out there.

1. Write down what you are proud of yourself for, in regards to your spiritual journey.

2. Write down a declaration giving yourself permission to be on your own path. This might look like: I am allowed to believe whatever I want to believe. It is okay for my journey to look different than others. I have the freedom to explore whatever draws me and feels good to my soul. Then sign at the bottom, like a contract with yourself.

More About The Spiritual Closet

The Safest Place Possible

A Powerful Mantra

As you move through your day, I hope you meet yourself
with love. You were made for this. It is who you are,
and it is what will heal, free, and empower you.

Exercise: List 10 thoughts/fears you have that make you
feel sad or anxious. Acknowledge each one, and then meet it
with love by simply saying, "I love you ".

Here are some examples:
I'm scared I'll never lose the weight I want to. — "I love you"
I'm scared I'm going to be homeless — "I love you"

1.

2.

3.

4.

5.

6.

7.

8.

9.

10.

More About A Powerful Mantra

DebbieMirza.com The Safest Place Possible

No Judgment

Exercise: Write down 10 things you judge about yourself, things you wish were different about you.

After you have written all of them down, go through each one and add, "No Judgment, <u>your name</u>." Say the words out loud to reinforce this new way of thinking and being to your brain. Allow yourself to feel how good it feels to be free from judgment and harsh thinking.

1.

2.

3.

4.

5.

6.

7.

8.

9.

10.

     The Safest Place Possible

More About No Judgment

Mirror Work

Much love and compassion to you today, dear reader.

Exercise: Look into your eyes in the mirror. Ask these questions and record your answers below.

1. What are you feeling right now? Thank you. What else?

2. What do you wish I would do differently to take care of you? What do you need from me? Thank you. What else?

Allow a conversation to flow. Be kind to yourself, empathetic, loving, and respectful. Give yourself permission to feel whatever comes up for you. Tears may come. They often do in this exercise. Record any part of the conversation that you would like to remember below, to help you know what you need right now.

More About Mirror Work

_____

_____

_____

_____

_____

_____

_____

_____

_____

_____

_____

_____

_____

_____

_____

DebbieMirza.com The Safest Place Possible

What Do I Wish They Would Do

Exercise: Think of someone right now who is irritating you, or you feel hurt by.

How do you wish this person would treat you? (Examples: I wish they would treat me with respect. I wish they trusted me. I wish they would listen to me more)

Now take those statements you just wrote above and write a letter to yourself from your soul. For example, "Dear Debbie, I need you to treat me with more respect. I need you to trust me more. I need you to listen to me more. Signed, your soul".

Add anyone else that is affecting you in a negative way in your life and repeat the exercise below.

More About What Do I Wish They Would Do

I'm Still Here

The next time you feel fear or sadness or anxiety, I hope you remind yourself you are still here and you are not going anywhere. You are here to listen, to love, and to embrace every part of you. You are worth the time, worth the love.

You deserve nothing less.

You were made for this.

Exercise: Reassure yourself that you are still here for you and will always be.

1. What is something you are ready to let go of in your life?

2. Ask your angels, God, the Universe, whoever you pray to for help with this.

3. Write a letter of commitment below, letting yourself know that you are still here and will always be here to listen, guide, and love every part of you.

More About I'm Still Here

Aftermath

Exercise: Make a list of at least 10 things you are doing really well in life right now. Be extraordinarily generous with yourself here. Your tribe is surrounding you with very proud smiles on each of their faces.

1.

2.

3.

4.

5.

6.

7.

8.

9.

10.

More About Aftermath

DebbieMirza.com The Safest Place Possible

Reconnecting With Your Soul

May you feel the freedom to feel all that is within you.
You are worth being heard.

Exercise: This is a chance for you to let your full self out. It will be a cathartic process for you. Allow the adult in you to step aside for this and invite the child in you that is lying on the floor crying or pounding his/her fists to come forth.

This is a chance for you to get really honest. It may be uncomfortable for you. But keep going. You are safe and are becoming an incredible caretaker for yourself.

Write down any and all honest feelings below. Write about how you are really feeling about your life right now. Let the tears, anger, frustration all pour out. You are safe. This is not the time for you to fix anything. This is time to purge. So, whatever comes to you, write it all down.

Reconnecting With Your Soul, continued

More About Reconnecting With Your Soul

DebbieMirza.com The Safest Place Possible

The Magic of Dropping Labels

Welcome to your magical body and world you live in.

1. Look around the room you are in and choose one object to look at. It may have a name like candle, lamp, or chair. Keep looking at it and drop the label. Imagine it has no name attached to it. Then sit with that and notice how it looks to you now, how your body feels seeing it without a name. Record what you notice below.

2. Now go outside and do the same thing with something in nature. Record below.

3. Feel free to keep going with this for as many things as you want, especially outside if you can. There is something about being in nature that calms and feeds our soul. Do you notice yourself feeling more present? More calm inside? Does the world seem more alive and magical to you?

More About The Magic of Dropping Labels

My Prayer Tonight

May you feel comforted and loved today. May you come to the realization your divine helpers are ready and willing to help with whatever you need and long for. May you be able to feel the peace that resides within you and is connected to others around you. You were made for peace and connection. May you recognize how valued you are today.

Exercise: Fill in the blanks and pray this prayer to whomever you pray, if this is something that draws you.

Angels, this is what I'm feeling right now. I'm feeling things around:

_____

_____

_____

_____

I'm scared of_____

_____

_____.

I'm also scared that _____

_____

_____.

I feel hurt that _____

_____

_____.

I feel sad about _____

_____

_____.

I ask for your help right now with all these things. I want to recognize truth. I want to be clear about the areas that feel jumbled and confusing. I want to find and experience peace with all of it. I want to see clearly instead of feeling lost.

I want to let go of thoughts and ingrained beliefs that are keeping me frozen, holding me back from being myself and doing what I came here to do.

I ask for your help now in reminding me of who I am and why I am here. I want to see easily what I need to see at this moment.

Please do what is in your power to help me with all these things.

Thank you for being here. Thank you for helping. Thank you for loving me and knowing me in ways I cannot see.

More About My Prayer Tonight

The Safest Place Possible

What To Do With The Stories

You are worth taking the time to be heard.
You are worthy of peace, worthy of calm.
Be the safe space for yourself that you so deserve.

Exercise: Recognize the story and go to the feeling. All you need to do here is get to the feeling. This will help you get more present and the story will feel less powerful.

1. Write down the story you are telling yourself about money. What is the feeling that comes out in you from this story?

2. What is the story you are telling yourself about your appearance? What is the feeling?

3. What is the story you are telling yourself about romantic relationships? What is the feeling?

4. Keep going with other stories you tell yourself in your life if you'd like and then acknowledge the feeling.

More About What To Do With The Stories

DebbieMirza.com The Safest Place Possible

Being Your Own Hero

There are things about you, often little things you do, ways
that you are, that are heroic.
Thank you for the beautiful things you bring to this world.
Thank you for taking the time to love on yourself.

Doing this exercise changes your energy and, in turn, affects
the people and the world around you, and we thank you for
that.

Exercise: List 10 ways in which you are your own hero.

1.

2.

3.

4.

5.

6.

7.

8.

9.

10.

More About Being Your Own Hero

DebbieMirza.com The Safest Place Possible

What Do You REALLY Want?

You are here for a reason.
You have something very special about you.
I wish I could hear about it right now.
I wish we could all sit in a circle and
hear each other's precious dreams.

Know that you are not alone.
I am smiling right now thinking about you
doing what you long to do.
I'm a big fan and can't wait to see you shine.

Here are some questions to help you get clear on what it is you really want to do in this life:

Who are you jealous of and why?

What things did you enjoy playing as a child and adolescent?

What do you find yourself doing where you lose track of time?

What stories do you like to hear about how certain people got to where they are?

Who seems like they have such a great life? What appears great about their life to you?

If you could magically create a life with your rules, what would it look like?

What books, articles, and TV shows do you gravitate to?

What are you scared to say out loud that you really would like to do with your life?

What imprint do you want to leave on this earth?

If you knew you wouldn't fail, what would you do?

If you were an observer watching you live your life, how would you finish this sentence? "Oh, I hope he/she does _____ while they are here. I'd be really bummed if they didn't get to do that."

More About What Do You REALLY Want?

The Safest Place Possible

Well Done!

I love the fact that you went through this workbook! I hope it helped you connect with yourself in a warm and loving way. You deserve that. You are a brave, beautiful human being and I love that you are here!

I'm so proud of you!

Much love to you today lovely one.

Warmly,

Debbie Mirza

Printed in Great Britain
by Amazon